In My Town

Kasia Reay

Illustrated by Lucy Banaji

Schofield&Sims

In my <u>ow</u>n I can h<u>ear</u> n<u>ear</u> and f<u>ar</u>.

I can h<u>ear</u> a van z<u>oo</u>mi<u>ng</u> d<u>ow</u>n the r<u>oa</u>d.

I can h<u>ear</u> a man y<u>e</u><u>ll</u><u>i</u><u>ng</u> in the m<u>ar</u>ket...

and a dog b<u>ar</u>ki<u>ng</u> in the p<u>ar</u>k.

In my t<u>ow</u>n I can h<u>ear</u> a balloon
goi<u>ng</u> pop,

men n<u>ear</u> a <u>sh</u>op...

and a fox howling in the dark.